Ron Rabbit has a new job. He is a milkman.

Ron has to get up at six. The sun is not up yet.

Ron fills his van with milk. Then he sets off.

clink clink

Mrs Jessop needs one bottle of milk. Ron dumps it on the step.

Two bottles for Miss Quin. Three bottles for Mr Chang.

Mr and Mrs Preston have ten
children. They need ten bottles
of milk!

Ron is getting the bottles from his van when he sees a man. The man is creeping along.

Is it Mr Preston? No, this man is not as thin, and he has a big black sack on his back.

When the man sees Ron he runs. "Stop!" yells Ron. He runs after the man.

Ron trips the man up. The man drops the sack and Ron grabs it. The man runs off.

In the sack are lots of things...
a clock, a pink jug, a big cup, a
green lamp, and a cash box!

Ron rings the bell. Mrs Preston is cross. "I was asleep, Ron," she says.

But then she sees all the things, and Ron tells her about the bad man. "Thank you, Ron!" says Mrs Preston.

Mr Preston rings the cops.

The cops catch the bad man.

Ron gets a medal.